Composers Series

A Bit of a Blow

for clarinet and piano

Brian Chapple

Bosworth

ISBN 978-1-78305-665-1

© Copyright 1999 Bosworth & Co. Ltd.
Published in Great Britain by Bosworth and Company
Limited
Head office:14-15 Berners Street,
London W1T 3LJ

Tel +44 (0)20 7612 7400
Fax +44 (0)20 7612 7546

Sales and Hire:
Music Sales Distribution Centre,
Newmarket Road,
Bury St Edmunds,
Suffolk IP33 3YB

Tel +44 (0)1284 702600
Fax +44 (0)1284 768301

www.musicsales.com
e-mail: music@musicsales.co.uk

A Bit of a Blow was originally written for the Saxology Quartet in 1996 and has been recorded by them on Meridian ('English Quartets' – CDE 84376). The version for clarinet and piano received its première on 5th June 1999 at St. John the Baptist, Chipping Barnet, performed by David Kirby with the composer at the piano; it was subsequently heard at the Edinburgh International Festival on 29 August 1999, with David Kirby accompanied by Gareth Hunt.

I made this arrangement for clarinet and piano in 1998; I am grateful to David Kirby for his practical advice.

Brian Chapple

A Bit of a Blow

Brian Chapple

I

Allegro giocoso (♩ = *c*.132) **with swing**

International copyright secured.

4

II

poch. movendo

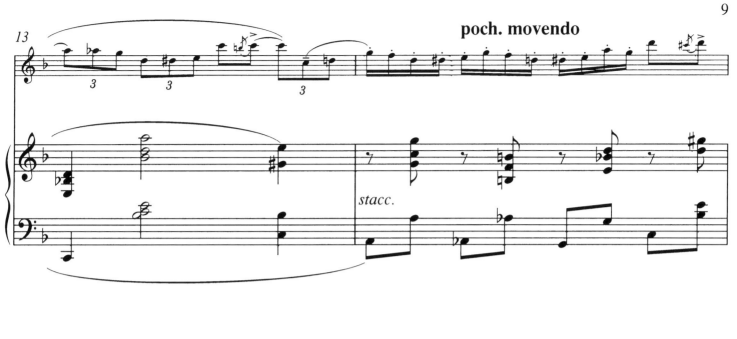

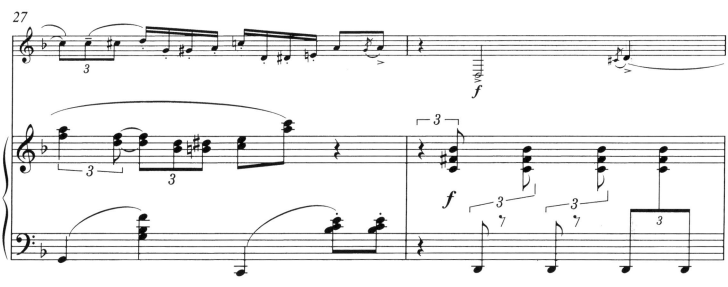

poch. movendo

III

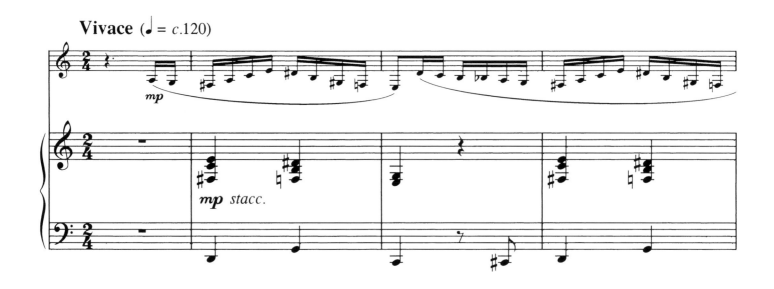

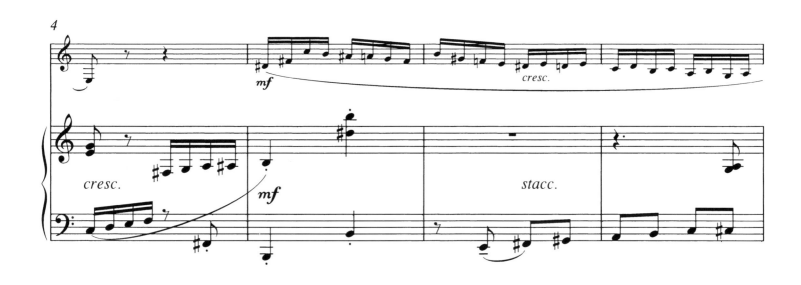

A Bit of a Blow

for clarinet and piano

Brian Chapple

Bosworth

A Bit of a Blow

CLARINET in B♭

Brian Chapple

I

Allegro giocoso (♩ = *c*.132) **with swing** ♪♩=♩♪

II

III

IV

V

Allegro con moto ($\quarternote$ = *c.*144) **with swing**

IV

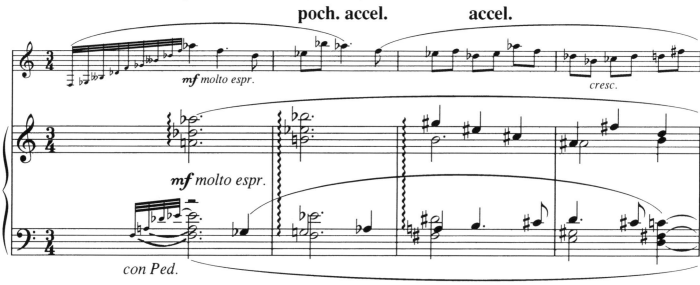

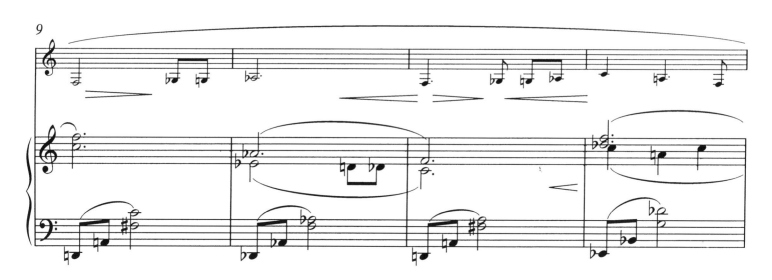

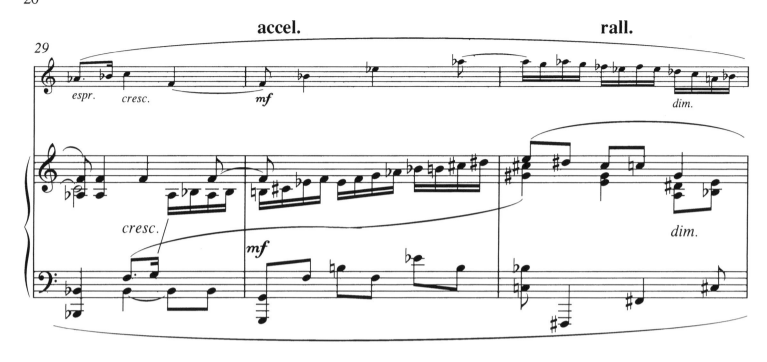

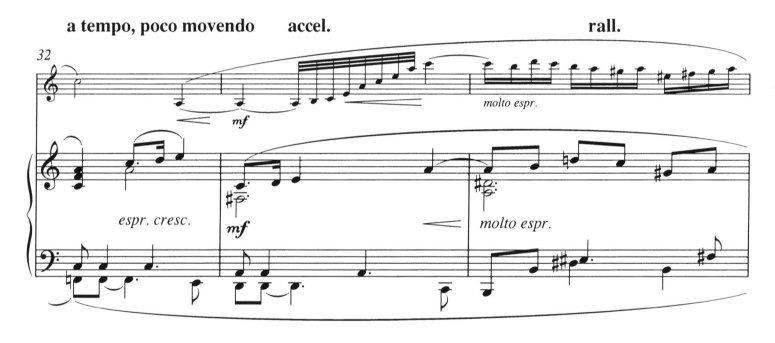

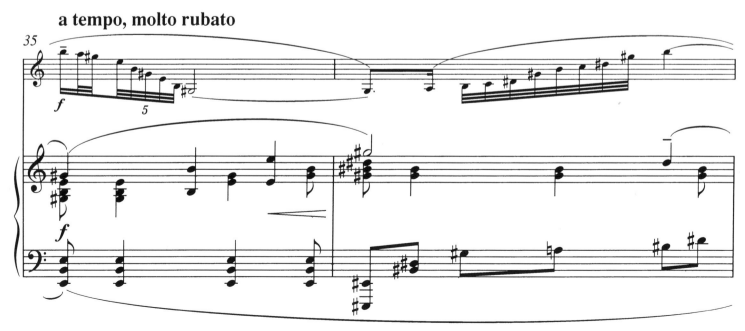

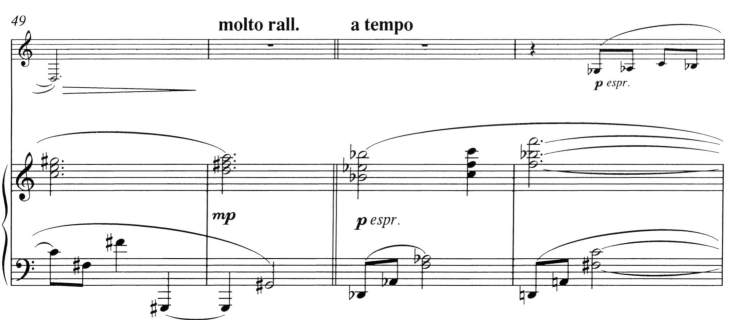

V